~~Content's~~

Contents

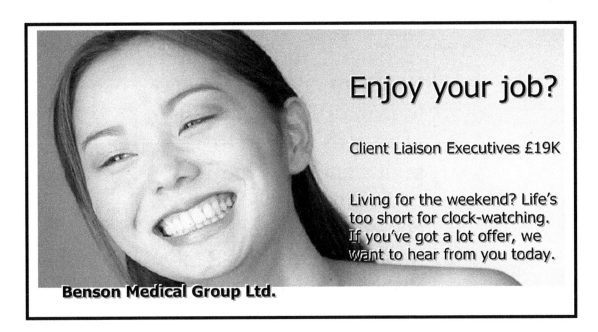

(Extract adapted from a job advert from an international financial organisation)

What kind of mistake do you see? (Tick one)

☐ apostrophes   ☐ articles

☐ doesn't make sense   ☐ punctuation

☐ singular / plural   ☐ spelling

Write your corrected version below:

_____

_____

_____

_____

_____

_____

Above all, the fish tasted excellent, although it was too small! The the chips were also cooked to a high standard. Taking everything into consideration, this reviewer feels that Paul's Fish Bar is well worth a look.

(Extract adapted from a local newspaper's "Eating Out" guide)

What kind of mistake do you see? (Tick one)

☐ apostrophes ☐ articles

☐ doesn't make sense ☐ punctuation

☐ singular / plural ☐ spelling

Write your corrected version below:

_____

_____

_____

_____

_____

_____

> **Please contact us ...**
>
> **if you have an Event that you would like us to feature in the next issue of Nature Journal Monthly. The deadline for submitting information for the May/June issue is April 3rd.**
>
> **Thank you.**

(Extract adapted from an article in a local hand-delivered magazine)

What kind of mistake do you see? (Tick one)

☐ apostrophes   ☐ articles

☐ doesn't make sense   ☐ punctuation

☐ singular / plural   ☐ spelling

Write your corrected version below:

_____

_____

_____

_____

_____

_____

QUICK KIDS' QUIZ

1. S _ E _ P
2. C _ W
3. H _ R _ E
4. C _ I _ K _ N
5. P _ G

O E I S H O H C E

These unfortunate letters have 'fallen out of the words above them and got mixed up together. Can you identify the five farmyard friends?

(Extract adapted from a local carnival brochure)

What kind of mistake do you see? (Tick one)

☐ apostrophes   ☐ articles

☐ doesn't make sense   ☐ punctuation

☐ singular / plural   ☐ spelling

Write your corrected version below:

_____

_____

_____

_____

_____

_____

Sir –

I would like to extend my heartfelt thanks to the staff and passengers at Heathrow Airport who came to my assistance when I was unfortunate enough to suffer a fall prior to departing on holiday on Thursday 12th May. I was assisted by a small group of cabin crew who happened to be passing when I fell. I should thank Irina in particular, for staying with me for well over an hour and ensuring that I caught my flight on time. It is heartening in this day and age to know that such kindness exists even in a place such as an crowded airport. I was able to continue my journey as planned and arrive the other end with "no harm done". My son would also like to extend his grateful thanks.

Sincerely, Laura Friedman, London

(Extract adapted from a letter published in a national newspaper)

What kind of mistake do you see? (Tick one)

☐ apostrophes ☐ articles

☐ doesn't make sense ☐ punctuation

☐ singular / plural ☐ spelling

Write your corrected version below:

_____

_____

_____

_____

_____

> This creatures
> name starts with
> the letter b...

(Extract adapted from a picture book aimed at pre-school children)

What kind of mistake do you see? (Tick one)

- ☐ apostrophes
- ☐ doesn't make sense
- ☐ singular / plural

- ☐ articles
- ☐ punctuation
- ☐ spelling

Write your corrected version below:

_____

_____

_____

_____

_____

_____

You're clearly spend a lot of time researching and preparing for roles …

Yes, I think it's important if you want to look authentic in the role. Sometimes it would be easier to just turn up on the first day of shooting and do … whatever the director asks you to do. But you should push yourself in life. You have to try harder. That's how you get better results.

(Extract adapted from a popular British film monthly)

What kind of mistake do you see? (Tick one)

☐ apostrophes   ☐ articles

☐ doesn't make sense   ☐ punctuation

☐ singular / plural   ☐ spelling

Write your corrected version below:

_____

_____

_____

_____

_____

BEST FOOD!

NO BODY BEATS US

QUALITY
SANDWICHES
& PIES

FROM

£1.29

EACH

(Extract adapted from a painted sign outside a sandwich shop in York)

What kind of mistake do you see? (Tick one)

☐ apostrophes   ☐ articles

☐ doesn't make sense   ☐ punctuation

☐ singular / plural   ☐ spelling

Write your corrected version below:

_____

_____

_____

_____

_____

_____

(Extract adapted from an advert in a catalogue picked up at a national high-street store)

What kind of mistake do you see? (Tick one)

☐ apostrophes   ☐ articles

☐ doesn't make sense   ☐ punctuation

☐ singular / plural   ☐ spelling

Write your corrected version below:

_____

_____

_____

_____

_____

_____

NEVER GO BACK

HARRIET CLARKE

21/08/06

'This album is an absolute joy.'
Music Times

An astonishing new collection.'
New Jazz Monthly

iQ
records

(Extract adapted from an advert in a national newspaper)

What kind of mistake do you see? (Tick one)

- ☐ apostrophes
- ☐ doesn't make sense
- ☐ singular / plural

- ☐ articles
- ☐ punctuation
- ☐ spelling

Write your corrected version below:

_____

_____

_____

_____

_____

_____

> Of course, nobody expects politicians to make nice, spend time in their constituency listening to the likes of you and me, *and* save the planet all in the same week. But it would be wonderful if we could rely on them to actually appear in the House of Commons every once in a while. If only to remind themselves where it is.

(Extract adapted from a column in a national newspaper's weekend magazine)

What kind of mistake do you see? (Tick one)

☐ apostrophes   ☐ articles

☐ doesn't make sense   ☐ punctuation

☐ singular / plural   ☐ spelling

Write your corrected version below:

_____

_____

_____

_____

_____

_____

Shaw's House Museum

ADMISSION FREE

Opening Hours:

Wednesday to Sunday
11am – 4.30pm

Shaws House Museum,
41 The Strand, Bakersfield,
Derbyshire, DE48 2SB

01332 406 9865

(Extract adapted from a city council leaflet advertising a public museum)

What kind of mistake do you see? (Tick one)

☐ apostrophes   ☐ articles

☐ doesn't make sense   ☐ punctuation

☐ singular / plural   ☐ spelling

Write your corrected version below:

_____

_____

_____

_____

_____

_____

The Shepherdsfield Carnival Committee would like to thank Sarah Blythe and Robin Everett of "Hair and Beauty World" on the High Street for generously providing:

Carnival Queens hair
Carnival Queens outfit
Carnival Queens make-up
Carnival Queens shoes

(Extract adapted from a seaside town's annual carnival brochure)

What kind of mistake do you see? (Tick one)

☐ apostrophes ☐ articles

☐ doesn't make sense ☐ punctuation

☐ singular / plural ☐ spelling

Write your corrected version below:

_____

_____

_____

_____

_____

_____

B.

(Extract adapted from a pop-up ad on the website of an internationally-famous internet service provider)

What kind of mistake do you see? (Tick one)

☐ apostrophes   ☐ articles

☐ doesn't make sense   ☐ punctuation

☐ singular / plural   ☐ spelling

Write your corrected version below:

_____

_____

_____

_____

_____

_____

The restaurant was packed and we were initially unsure whether we would get in, but eventually a harassed-looking waitress appeared and showed us to our table, which was pleasantly situated near a large bay window, with an enchanting view of the Japanese gardens and a an adventure playground, where a group of small children were evidently making full use of all the facilities!

(Extract adapted from an article in a local newspaper's "Eating Out" guide)

What kind of mistake do you see? (Tick one)

☐ apostrophes ☐ articles

☐ doesn't make sense ☐ punctuation

☐ singular / plural ☐ spelling

Write your corrected version below:

_____

_____

_____

_____

_____

_____

Around Birmingham

When it comes to Birmingham city centre there are an unbelievable variety of things to do. If you enjoy bargain-hunting at all the latest stores, why not try the New Bull Ring Centre – a shrine to good shopping! There are also many opportunities to get cultural. Whether you enjoy museums, galleries, cinemas, or just chilling out in chic little bars and eateries, Birmingham city centre has – rather astonishingly – got the lot!

(Extract adapted from an article in a local newspaper's "What's On?" guide)

What kind of mistake do you see? (Tick one)

☐ apostrophes ☐ articles

☐ doesn't make sense ☐ punctuation

☐ singular / plural ☐ spelling

Write your corrected version below:

_____

_____

_____

_____

_____

_____

Go to work on an egg …

EGGS – BRITAIN'S BREAKFAST FAVOURITES

THE HUMBLE egg has come top of a survey that lists the top ten breakfast foods among British families. In a new survey, by NewPoll, more than 45 per cent said they "often" ate a hard-boiled egg and soldiers before setting off for work, while a whopping 55 per cent of those said they had didn't want to contemplate a day at the grindstone without tucking into a home-cooked breakfast first.

(Extract adapted from an article in a national tabloid newspaper)

What kind of mistake do you see? (Tick one)

☐ apostrophes ☐ articles

☐ doesn't make sense ☐ punctuation

☐ singular / plural ☐ spelling

Write your corrected version below:

_____

_____

_____

_____

_____

Tapescript 4.1:

L = Leanne   C = Carolyn

L: Hello, Madam. Are you looking for anything in particular?

C: I need a new skirt for a job interview. But it must match this jacket.

L: What about his one? It's the same colour.

C: No, I think it's a bit too dark.

L: Well what about this one?

C: Yes, that looks like a good match. Can I try it on?

(Extract adapted from a course book for students of English as a Foreign Language, published by a major UK publisher of English language teaching materials)

What kind of mistake do you see? (Tick one)

☐ apostrophes   ☐ articles

☐ doesn't make sense   ☐ punctuation

☐ singular / plural   ☐ spelling

Write your corrected version below:

_____

_____

_____

_____

_____

_____

B.

Classic

Since the dresses are meant to be classic and elegant, its designers have spent a lot of time trying out different colours and fabrics.

(Extract adapted from an article in a national newspaper)

What kind of mistake do you see? (Tick one)

☐ apostrophes   ☐ articles

☐ doesn't make sense   ☐ punctuation

☐ singular / plural   ☐ spelling

Write your corrected version below:

_____

_____

_____

_____

_____

_____

Mr. Newell said on Friday, "Unfortunately, due to a continuous slowdown in demand for our products, we have had no choice but to offer voluntary redundancy packages. These will come into force from the September 20th. It is hoped that less than a quarter of our current workforce will be affected."

(Extract adapted from an article in a local newspaper's business pages)

What kind of mistake do you see? (Tick one)

☐ apostrophes ☐ articles

☐ doesn't make sense ☐ punctuation

☐ singular / plural ☐ spelling

Write your corrected version below:

_____

_____

_____

_____

_____

_____

Special Offer – Hurry While Stocks Last!
12 months half price line rental*

*Terms and conditions apply

(Extract adapted from a catalogue produced by a major high-street store)

What kind of mistake do you see? (Tick one)

☐ apostrophes   ☐ articles

☐ doesn't make sense   ☐ punctuation

☐ singular / plural   ☐ spelling

Write your corrected version below:

_____

_____

_____

_____

_____

_____

Gill's gang of misfits has confounded its critics by returning with a totally barnstorming collection of classic funk sounds. The problem is that they just don't seem to know when to stop! They seem inable to know when it's time to end a track. Some of the tunes rumble on for upwards of quarter of an hour, before ending completely without warning, as if someone has simply pulled the plug out of their "Funk Machine".

(Extract adapted from a national newspaper's "What's On?" guide)

What kind of mistake do you see? (Tick one)

☐ apostrophes   ☐ articles

☐ doesn't make sense   ☐ punctuation

☐ singular / plural   ☐ spelling

Write your corrected version below:

_____

_____

_____

_____

_____

_____

EAGLE
by Thomas Hannigan

"Lord of the skies, warrior, predator, theif, cold-blooded killer ... the eagle is all of these things."

(Extract adapted from the cover of a book by a well-known author)

What kind of mistake do you see? (Tick one)

☐ apostrophes   ☐ articles

☐ doesn't make sense   ☐ punctuation

☐ singular / plural   ☐ spelling

Write your corrected version below:

_____

_____

_____

_____

_____

_____

WHAT WOULD YOU SAY TO 6 WEEKS FREE DVD RENTAL?

(Extract adapted from promotional material for a well-known online DVD rental company)

What kind of mistake do you see? (Tick one)

- ☐ apostrophes
- ☐ doesn't make sense
- ☐ singular / plural
- ☐ articles
- ☐ punctuation
- ☐ spelling

Write your corrected version below:

_____

_____

_____

_____

_____

_____

Get ready for the last word in home entertainment!

It's coming! The CHANNEL HOPPA is the ultimate digital gadget and this year's must-have Christmas gift. It's fully portable, so no matter where you are or what you're doing you'll have easy access to all your music, games films and photos – instantly!

(Extract adapted from a promotional campaign by a national high-street chain)

What kind of mistake do you see? (Tick one)

☐ apostrophes   ☐ articles

☐ doesn't make sense   ☐ punctuation

☐ singular / plural   ☐ spelling

Write your corrected version below:

_____

_____

_____

_____

_____

_____

Owen bounces back to number one

Veteran Welsh rocker Owen Williams has stormed straight to the top of the UK singles chart, with his latest release Never Be Lonely (When You've Got A Friend).

It is the first track to be taken from his new greatest hits album, which is released on Monday. The album has been hotly anticipated by fans, but seen by music critic as marking the end of Williams's long and distinguished pop career.

Williams commented last night: "There's life in the old dog yet. I hope I've still got one or two more hits in me." His greatest hits album includes eleven UK number one singles.

(Extract adapted from an entertainment news website published by a national broadcaster)

What kind of mistake do you see? (Tick one)

☐ apostrophes

☐ doesn't make sense

☐ singular / plural

☐ articles

☐ punctuation

☐ spelling

Write your corrected version below:

_____

_____

_____

_____

_____

_____

(Extract adapted from an onscreen logo on a popular music TV channel)

What kind of mistake do you see? (Tick one)

☐ apostrophes   ☐ articles

☐ doesn't make sense   ☐ punctuation

☐ singular / plural   ☐ spelling

Write your corrected version below:

_____

_____

_____

_____

_____

_____

Parkinson describes writing new history as "labour of love"

Historian Daniel Parkinson has said that he took fifteen years to write a new book about the Battle of Trafalgar as simply being one of artistic integrity. In "Love, Death and Glory at Trafalgar" Parkinson claims to bring new insights into the strategies employed by Admiral Lord Nelson. He explained: "The new book has taken so long because there are so many sources available and I like to immerse myself in all of them. What is the great hurry, after all? Writing should be a leisurely process. It takes time for thoughts and hypotheses to ferment and come together."

(Extract adapted from a news article on a website published by a national broadcaster)

What kind of mistake do you see? (Tick one)

☐ apostrophes   ☐ articles

☐ doesn't make sense   ☐ punctuation

☐ singular / plural   ☐ spelling

Write your corrected version below:

_____

_____

_____

_____

_____

WOMENS CLOTHES SALE

All items are end-of-line stock from a major high-street store and will be discounted by at least 60%. Grab a bargain!

TUESDAY 18th OCTOBER

AT

St. Faith's Parish Hall, Bakersfield

(Extract adapted from a leaflet distributed at a Further Education college in the Midlands)

What kind of mistake do you see? (Tick one)

- [ ] apostrophes
- [ ] doesn't make sense
- [ ] singular / plural
- [ ] articles
- [ ] punctuation
- [ ] spelling

Write your corrected version below:

_____

_____

_____

_____

_____

_____

I spent a relaxing afternoon wandering the impressive malls and tiny boutiques on George Street and around Macquarie Place, before sampling some culture at the Museum of Contemporary Art. A few minutes and a short cab ride later, I was strolling along Bondi Beach, trouser legs rolled up to the ankle; suddenly part of the Aussie beach scene. Sydney, it seemed was a city of striking contrasts.

(Extract adapted from a best-selling travel book)

What kind of mistake do you see? (Tick one)

☐ apostrophes   ☐ articles

☐ doesn't make sense   ☐ punctuation

☐ singular / plural   ☐ spelling

Write your corrected version below:

_____

_____

_____

_____

_____

_____

> **Sunday 16th April!!!!**
>
> Yes, we know it's still some way off, but we are announcing the date of our AGM early in an attempt to allow the busier members of our congregation to get it booked into their diaries well in advance. This year, for the first time, we will be holding the AGM as part of our 10.45 am morning service.

(Extract adapted from a service sheet distributed at a Midlands cathedral)

What kind of mistake do you see? (Tick one)

☐ apostrophes   ☐ articles

☐ doesn't make sense   ☐ punctuation

☐ singular / plural   ☐ spelling

Write your corrected version below:

_____

_____

_____

_____

_____

_____

10.30 News Report (T) 223478
11.20 Make Me Rich (T) (R)
The team of fiery business gurus is back to help members of the public launch their business plans. Tonight, a student from Wales has a idea for turning derelict properties into suburban palaces.

(Extract adapted from a national newspaper's TV guide)

What kind of mistake do you see? (Tick one)

☐ apostrophes   ☐ articles

☐ doesn't make sense   ☐ punctuation

☐ singular / plural   ☐ spelling

Write your corrected version below:

_____

_____

_____

_____

_____

_____

What's the chances ofa mannedmission to Mas?

(Extract adapted from a headline in a well-known national magazine for teachers)

What kind of mistake do you see? (Tick one)

☐ apostrophes   ☐ articles

☐ doesn't make sense   ☐ punctuation

☐ singular / plural   ☐ spelling

Write your corrected version below:

_____

_____

_____

_____

_____

_____

(Extract adapted from an advert in a local paper for a major high-street store)

What kind of mistake do you see? (Tick one)

☐ apostrophes   ☐ articles

☐ doesn't make sense   ☐ punctuation

☐ singular / plural   ☐ spelling

Write your corrected version below:

_____

_____

_____

_____

_____

_____

Improve a
Childs Life

Derbyshire Foundation for Children
Annual Appeal

(Extract adapted from a leaflet advertising a fundraising appeal by a regional charity)

What kind of mistake do you see? (Tick one)

☐ apostrophes   ☐ articles

☐ doesn't make sense   ☐ punctuation

☐ singular / plural   ☐ spelling

Write your corrected version below:

_____

_____

_____

_____

_____

_____

Table of British Prime Ministers

Sir Robert Walpole	1721-42	Whig
Earl of Wilmington	1742-43	Whig
Henry Pelham	1743-54	Whig
Duke of Newcastle	1754-56	Whig
Duke of Devonshire	1756-57	Whig
Duke of Newcastle	1757-62	Whig
Earl of Bute	1763-65	Tory
George Grenville	1762-63	Whig
Marquess of Rockingham	1765-66	Whig
Earl of Chatham	1766-68	Tory

(Extract adapted from an article in a national magazine for teachers)

What kind of mistake do you see? (Tick one)

☐ apostrophes   ☐ articles

☐ doesn't make sense   ☐ punctuation

☐ singular / plural   ☐ spelling

Write your corrected version below:

_____

_____

_____

_____

_____

_____

Baby
of the
Year '05

The Bakersfield Gazette's ever-popular Baby of the Year' competition is back

We're beginning our annual search for the bubbliest, bonniest baby in Bakersfield – and we want *you* to send us your cutest baby pictures!

(Extract adapted from a competition feature in a local newspaper)

What kind of mistake do you see? (Tick one)

- ☐ apostrophes
- ☐ doesn't make sense
- ☐ singular / plural
- ☐ articles
- ☐ punctuation
- ☐ spelling

Write your corrected version below:

_____

_____

_____

_____

_____

_____

CALLING ALL STUDENTS!

Apply today and get a free 4-year Young Persons Travel Card worth up to £250!

(Extract adapted from a promotional leaflet produced by a national bank)

What kind of mistake do you see? (Tick one)

☐ apostrophes   ☐ articles

☐ doesn't make sense   ☐ punctuation

☐ singular / plural   ☐ spelling

Write your corrected version below:

_____

_____

_____

_____

_____

_____

Once you have completed the course, you will be more fluent in French and be able to participate with confidence in all sorts of every day situations.

(Extract adapted from a course brochure by a national provider of online courses for adults)

What kind of mistake do you see? (Tick one)

☐ apostrophes   ☐ articles

☐ doesn't make sense   ☐ punctuation

☐ singular / plural   ☐ spelling

Write your corrected version below:

_____

_____

_____

_____

_____

_____

Bakersfield Museum & Art Gallery

Saturday 5th November
& Saturday 12th November

Come along to our arts and crafts open days. Children will have the chance make their own models and sculptures based on exhibits in the museum. Or come and paint a masterpiece - it might even be displayed in the main gallery!

Activities start at 10.30am and last for about 2 hours.
Admission free. All welcome!

(Extract adapted from a leaflet advertising a museum's activity days for children)

What kind of mistake do you see? (Tick one)

☐ apostrophes ☐ articles

☐ doesn't make sense ☐ punctuation

☐ singular / plural ☐ spelling

Write your corrected version below:

_____

_____

_____

_____

_____

_____

SIX FREE DVD RENTALS DELIVERED TO YOUR DOOR!

HERE'S HOW IT WORKS:

1. *Choose your DVDs online from 1000s of titles*

2. *Get your DVDs through the post – sent by first class mail*

3. *Watch your DVDs and keep them as long as you like – no late fees!*

4. *Post back your DVDs using pre-paid envelopes and we'll lsend you more!*

(Extract adapted from a promotional leaflet by a well-known DVD rental company)

What kind of mistake do you see? (Tick one)

 apostrophes

☐ articles

☐ doesn't make sense

☐ punctuation

☐ singular / plural

☐ spelling

Write your corrected version below:

_____

_____

_____

_____

_____

_____

GREAT PHOTOS
FROM DIGITAL
IN ONLY 1 HOUR!

Simply bring your digital media
to our store, review your pictures
on screen and choose the one's
you want. It's so easy!

(Extract adapted from a brochure produced by a national photo-processing store)

What kind of mistake do you see? (Tick one)

☐ apostrophes ☐ articles

☐ doesn't make sense ☐ punctuation

☐ singular / plural ☐ spelling

Write your corrected version below:

_____

_____

_____

_____

_____

_____

What the Heritage Committee is doing about it?

People Against Pollution is the latest Heritage Committee campaign, which aims to reduce levels of pollution in the areas around buildings or sites of special historical or cultural significance.

(Extract adapted from a lavish promotional booklet produced by a national campaign group)

What kind of mistake do you see? (Tick one)

☐ apostrophes ☐ articles

☐ doesn't make sense ☐ punctuation

☐ singular / plural ☐ spelling

Write your corrected version below:

_____

_____

_____

_____

_____

_____

By Christmas, owners of the new Channel Hoppa console will have a much high quality selection of games and movies from which to choose. At present they are limited to the initial launch range of just thirty games and twenty movie titles. More of both types of entertainment are slated to be rush-released at the beginning of next month, just in time for the lucrative Christmas market. So if you bought a Hoppa on day one and were disappointed by the lack of titles available, watch this space!

(Extract adapted from an article in a national newspaper)

What kind of mistake do you see? (Tick one)

☐ apostrophes ☐ articles

☐ doesn't make sense ☐ punctuation

☐ singular / plural ☐ spelling

Write your corrected version below:

_____

_____

_____

_____

_____

_____

Discover South West Derbyshire!

Tired of the stresses and strains of city life?In South West Derbyshire you can leave it all behind and get lost in the beautiful hills and wide-open spaes.Enjoy the cultural delights of Ashbourne,a quiet market town known as the "Gateway to the Peak",which is only 6 minutes drive away from Junction 2of the M

(Extract adapted from a promotional brochure produced by a major British city's tourist board)

What kind of mistake do you see? (Tick one)

☐ apostrophes   ☐ articles

☐ doesn't make sense   ☐ punctuation

☐ singular / plural   ☐ spelling

Write your corrected version below:

_____

_____

_____

_____

_____

_____

Peking View Hotel

This year we are offering a special 3-day New Year's break for only £180 per person half board. Price includes full English breakfast each morning, a lavish New Year's Eve party and a special celebratory lunch on New Year's Day.

Lunch will be served on New Year's Day at 1 O'clock

(Extract adapted from a promotional leaflet available at a large country hotel)

What kind of mistake do you see? (Tick one)

☐ apostrophes ☐ articles

☐ doesn't make sense ☐ punctuation

☐ singular / plural ☐ spelling

Write your corrected version below:

_____

_____

_____

_____

_____

_____

Bloomin' Marvellous Work!

The Shepherdsfield Young Liberal Democrats have been labouring away in the garden all summer long, organising a successful clean-up campaign that has transformed the gardens of more than a hundred elderly or infirm people in the local area.

A small team of enthusiastic volunteers has spent the last four Saturdays pulling weeds, trimming lawns and planting shrubs. On the final day a competition was held to decide which gardens had undergone the greatest transformation. Local Liberal Democrat councillor Margaret Smeghurst handed over first prize of a bottle of bubbly to Mr& Mrs Halliwell, who live on Matlock Crescent, Morley Way.

(Extract adapted from an article in a local party political mailshot)

What kind of mistake do you see? (Tick one)

☐ apostrophes   ☐ articles

☐ doesn't make sense   ☐ punctuation

☐ singular / plural   ☐ spelling

Write your corrected version below:

_____

_____

_____

_____

_____

> # More than 50 fantastic live tracks from all your favourite bands!
>
> **DVD BONUS FEATURES:**
> - Interviews with Barry Shilton and Gordon Peel
> - Programme your 10 favourite tracks
> - Exclusive performances and never-before-seen footage of Caterpillar's famous "lost" gig

(Extract adapted from an advert for a DVD promoted by a national broadcaster)

What kind of mistake do you see? (Tick one)

☐ apostrophes   ☐ articles

☐ doesn't make sense   ☐ punctuation

☐ singular / plural   ☐ spelling

Write your corrected version below:

_____

_____

_____

_____

_____

South West Derbyshire College
Students' Union

The students' union is here to make your time at South West Derbyshire College that much more … *fun and funky!* We're also here to listen to your ideas and suggestions for improving facilities, and to fight your corner if you have any problems. The students' union has it's own facilities on both campuses, so why not come and say "Hi" sometime? We're a friendly bunch and we don't bite – well, Boz does, but we try to keep him busy working on the college's student radio station – SWDC FM!

(Extract adapted from an article in a prospectus produced by a large FE college)

What kind of mistake do you see? (Tick one)

☐ apostrophes

☐ doesn't make sense

☐ singular / plural

☐ articles

☐ punctuation

☐ spelling

Write your corrected version below:

_____

_____

_____

_____

_____

_____

The use of technology in the classroom has revolutionised the way some teachers work. Interactive whiteboards, digital television and the use of email to submit homework have transformed the way that students can engage with their classroom environment. Clear and effective communication is still the foremost priority in any teaching situation, but the way that students and teachers are now interacting – both with each other and the resources they have access to – has fundamentally changed. Above all this, means that many teachers have had to go "back to school" themselves and learn how to plug into the digital age. (A lesson that has been hard to learn for those who had only just begun to get to grips with the transition from blackboard and chalk to whiteboard and marker pen.)

(Extract adapted from an article in a national magazine for teachers)

What kind of mistake do you see? (Tick one)

☐ apostrophes   ☐ articles

☐ doesn't make sense   ☐ punctuation

☐ singular / plural   ☐ spelling

Write your corrected version below:

_____

_____

_____

_____

_____

For those of you who would rather set off sightseeing than sleep off a heavy night on a hot beach, there are a staggering amount of things to see on the island. Tours of the old town and market area leave the hotel reception every morning at 10.30am, returning in time for lunch at 1 o'clock.

(Extract adapted from a local newspaper's "What's On?" guide)

What kind of mistake do you see? (Tick one)

☐ apostrophes ☐ articles

☐ doesn't make sense ☐ punctuation

☐ singular / plural ☐ spelling

Write your corrected version below:

_____

_____

_____

_____

_____

_____

SUPER VALUE!

NEW! ONLY £6.99

Get the kid's little fingers active this Christmas with our fabulous, funky farm activity sets. They make fantastic stocking fillers and are great value at only £6.99 each (or 2 for £10.99).

(Extract adapted from a catalogue of toys for children published by a large retailer)

What kind of mistake do you see? (Tick one)

☐ apostrophes   ☐ articles

☐ doesn't make sense   ☐ punctuation

☐ singular / plural   ☐ spelling

Write your corrected version below:

_____

_____

_____

_____

_____

_____

Last Night's TV
With Carl Douglas

BBC 1, 8pm   Joe's Choice

I watched this sit-com for the first time last night and found it affable enough, although short on big belly laughs. The premise involves a brace of painter and decorators – former union leader Joe (played by Jack Dumas) and his mate Terry (Simon Sims). The bungling duo are to the decorating trade what a slap in the face is to a well-intentioned octogenarian. The laughs are supposed to spring from the eco-friendly duo attempting to put right their botched jobs in a way that's "ethical and doesn't leave much in the way of a global footprint" – Joe and Terry's motto. I got the feeling that Dumas is simply slumming it in this show, which is more of a vehicle for Sims and is trademark slapstick routines. Not one to avoid, but fairly forgettable. Carl's Choice – I'll probably give it a miss next time, I'm afraid.

(Extract adapted from an article in a national newspaper)

What kind of mistake do you see? (Tick one)

- ☐ apostrophes
- ☐ articles
- ☐ doesn't make sense
- ☐ punctuation
- ☐ singular / plural
- ☐ spelling

Write your corrected version below:

_____

_____

_____

_____

_____

(Extract adapted from a regular strip cartoon in a national newspaper)

What kind of mistake do you see? (Tick one)

- [ ] apostrophes
- [ ] doesn't make sense
- [ ] singular / plural
- [ ] articles
- [ ] punctuation
- [ ] spelling

Write your corrected version below:

_____

_____

_____

_____

_____

_____

> *Prayers – led by Marion & Graham Winter*
>
> *Reading from the New Testament*
>
> *A Easter Message*
>
> *Song – "He has Risen"*

(Extract adapted from a parish church's service sheet)

What kind of mistake do you see? (Tick one)

☐ apostrophes ☐ articles

☐ doesn't make sense ☐ punctuation

☐ singular / plural ☐ spelling

Write your corrected version below:

_____

_____

_____

_____

_____

_____

'Ello Jeff.

Want to buy a new laptop for £449.99?

Blue Danube Technology

(Extract adapted from a national newspaper advert produced by an international company)

What kind of mistake do you see? (Tick one)

☐ apostrophes   ☐ articles

☐ doesn't make sense   ☐ punctuation

☐ singular / plural   ☐ spelling

Write your corrected version below:

_____

_____

_____

_____

_____

_____

Assistant Box Office Manager

(Maternity Cover) £15,295

An exciting opportunity to contribute to the continuing success of one of the UK's leading theatres.

We are looking for candidates with two or more years of ticket or event sales experience. You will be an ambitious and well-motivated individual, who enjoys working with the general public and is keen to take on an assistant managment role.

(Extract adapted from a leaflet advertising job vacancies at a large provincial theatre)

What kind of mistake do you see? (Tick one)

- ☐ apostrophes
- ☐ doesn't make sense
- ☐ singular / plural
- ☐ articles
- ☐ punctuation
- ☐ spelling

Write your corrected version below:

_____

_____

_____

_____

_____

_____

(Extract adapted from a book of cartoons published by a major international publisher)

What kind of mistake do you see? (Tick one)

☐ apostrophes   ☐ articles

☐ doesn't make sense   ☐ punctuation

☐ singular / plural   ☐ spelling

Write your corrected version below:

_____

_____

_____

_____

_____

_____

People Power – Getting Results

I'm pleased to report that in the last couple of months we have been able to help more than 400 people find work. For many of those it was the first time they had been in employment for several years. Everyone at People Power everyone plays an enormously important role in helping ordinary people back into sustainable employment. A big thank you to all our staff in all our centres around the country. What you do really does change people's lives for the better.

With warm wishes to you all,

Marilyn

Marilyn Wormsley, Managing Director of People Power

(Extract adapted from a national training company's quarterly newsletter)

What kind of mistake do you see? (Tick one)

☐ apostrophes ☐ articles

☐ doesn't make sense ☐ punctuation

☐ singular / plural ☐ spelling

Write your corrected version below:

_____

_____

_____

_____

_____

_____

Owen keeps us grooving in the aisles!

Owen Williams – showman

REVIEW
Birmingham NEC

Fans at his sellout show in Birmingham gave Owen Williams an ecstatic response last night as he rolled back the years and treated us to a rock 'n' roll spectacular *par excellence*. It was like 1982 all over again as Williams sprinted energetically through all his memorable hits, as well as some superb new tunes. Sales of his latest release, Never Be Lonely (When You've Got A Friend), have now past the 2 million mark in the UK alone.

(Extract adapted from a promotional brochure by a national company)

What kind of mistake do you see? (Tick one)

☐ apostrophes		☐ articles
☐ doesn't make sense		☐ punctuation
☐ singular / plural		☐ spelling

Write your corrected version below:

_____

_____

_____

_____

_____

_____

Aswers

1. doesn't make sense

There is a "to" missing from the last sentence. It should read: "If you've got a lot *to* offer, we want to hear from you today."

2. doesn't make sense

In this example there is an unnecessary "the" in the second sentence, before "chips". The sentence should read: "The chips were also cooked to a high standard."

3. punctuation

The word "event" does not need a capital letter. It is a common noun, not a proper noun, and therefore should start with a small "e". In contrast, "Nature Journal Monthly" is the name of the magazine and as such is a proper noun and needs a capital letter at the start of each part of its name. "May", "June" and "April" are also proper nouns and should start with capital letters because they are names of months. "Please", "The" and "Thank" all start with a capital letter because they are the first words in their sentences.

4. punctuation

There is a stray single speech mark at the beginning of the word "fallen". Perhaps the author meant to write 'fallen out' in single speech marks, as a way of highlighting this phrase, but forgot to close the speech marks.

5. articles

The mistake is in the sentence which begins: "It is heartening in this day and age …" The author has written "*an* crowded airport" where it should read: "*a* crowded airport". The article "an" is only used when the word which follows it begins with a vowel sound, such as "an *o*range", "an *a*ccident" or "an *u*nexpected incident". The words which come after "an" in these examples – "orange", "accident" and "unexpected" – all start with a vowel sound: sounds made when using the vowels in English – a, e, i, o and u. The word "crowded" starts with a hard "c" sound, rather than a vowel sound, so it can't be preceded by the article "an". Article "a" is the right one to use.

6. apostrophes

In this example there is an apostrophe missing. There must be an apostrophe between "creature" and "s" to show possession – the "name" belongs to the "creature". It is the "creature's name". Without a possessive apostrophe the word "creatures" could be taken to be plural (more than one "creature"), which then wouldn't make sense in the sentence, because the first word "This …" is only used before singular words ("These" would be used before plural words, e.g. "This creature" and "These creatures"). Without the possessive apostrophe "s" after "creature", the meaning of the sentence is lost.

7. doesn't make sense

This is a case of an unnecessary verb. Instead of "You're" in the first sentence, the author should have simply used the personal subject pronoun "You".

8. spelling

The correct word the author of this sign was looking for here was "nobody", rather than two words "no body". If you have any doubts about how to spell a word, always check your dictionary.

9. apostrophes

It must be hard being called "Williams", because people often seem to get this name wrong when it comes to making it possessive. This superstar singing sensation's name is "Owen Williams". It says so in the advert. But in the title the author has altered his name to "Owen William", then added apostrophe "s" to make it possessive – the "Greatest Hits" belong to "Owen William". However, the "Greatest Hits" should belong to "Owen Williams", so the correct title should read: "Owen Williams's Greatest Hits" – the apostrophe "s" coming after the *full name* of this mega-selling balladeer. There are differing opinions about this. Some editors would favour "Owen Williams'" over "Owen Williams's", but "Owen William's" is completely wrong, because it alters the spelling of the singer's last name by missing off the final "s".

10. punctuation

Although the fictional magazine "New Jazz Monthly" really enjoyed this new album from the fictional sensitive singer-songwriter Harriet Clarke, their review in this print advertisement lacks a certain amount of credibility because there is a single speech mark missing from the beginning. It should read: 'An astonishing new collection'.

11. doesn't make sense

"Of course, nobody expects politicians to make nice ..." – to make nice what? Unfortunately, we will never know what the author intended to say, although perhaps the missing word was "speeches", or "policies". In this example there is a common noun missing after the adjective "nice". "Nice" is describing something, but what it describes is absent and instead we move breathlessly on to the next clause (or part) of the sentence.

12. apostrophes

In this example, the owners of the museum need to sit down and have a long think about what the name of their museum should be. In the title – "Shaw's House Museum" – they have used the apostrophe correctly: the "House", or even the "House Museum", belong to "Shaw" (whoever he or she is). But in the address section the name of the museum is unceremoniously stripped of its apostrophe to become plain old: "Shaws House Museum". Since consistency is one of the hallmarks of good writing, the author would be better off choosing one or the other of the two titles and sticking to it. I would favour the first – "Shaw's House Museum" – because it uses the possessive apostrophe "s" in a grammatically correct way. We know that "Shaw" is an English surname, so we can guess that the name of the museum indicates that the house (or the house museum) belongs to (or used to belong to) a person named Shaw. In which case, the author needs to use the possessive apostrophe "s".

13. apostrophes

This example is alarming because not only does it make an error with a possessive apostrophe "s" – it makes it worse by repeating the error three more times. We learn that "Hair and Beauty World" (on the High Street) have provided lots of goods and services for the Carnival Queen. These things now belong to the Carnival Queen, so we must show this possession – that the hair, outfit, make-up and shoes belong to her – by using an apostrophe "s" after "Carnival Queen" on each of the four occasions it is needed, e.g. "Carnival Queen*'s* hair", and so on.

14. spelling

This example came from an online pop-up advertisement on a website which was designed and created by someone working for one of the biggest multinational corporations on earth – which should give hope to the rest of us, who also sometimes make unnecessary spelling errors like this one. "Click to find *our* more" should, of course, read: "Click to find *out* more".

15. articles

The author of this report is hedging their bets by using both articles before the word "adventure", when choosing the right one for the job would be preferable! It should read: "… and *an* adventure playground". We need to use article "an" before "adventure" because "adventure" starts with a vowel sound – "a" for *a*ngry, *a*ggravated and *a*nteater.

16. singular / plural

There is a mix-up in the first sentence to do with using "there are" instead of "there is". It should read: "… there *is* an unbelievable variety of things to do". This mistake is understandable, because the second part of the sentence – "variety of things to do" – appears to indicate more than one thing – and makes the sentence look plural. Therefore the writer uses the plural verb "are" (from verb "to be") with "there" to form the structure "there are…". However, before the plural bit we can see a singular article "an" which overrides the end of the sentence and tells us that the subject of the sentence – "unbelievable variety of things to do" – is in actual fact singular. The main noun in this sentence – "variety" – is singular, despite the fact that it means many things. We would say "a variety of chocolates" (with singular article "a") not "some variety of chocolates" (with plural determiner "some"). Confusing, eh?

17. doesn't make sense

There is an unnecessary verb ("had") in the second sentence. It should read: "… a whopping 55 per cent of those said they didn't want to contemplate a day at the grindstone without tucking into a home-cooked breakfast first."

18. doesn't make sense

This example, from a tapescript written and produced by a leading UK publisher of English language teaching materials, doesn't make sense because there is one letter missing from the third speech. Leanne should say: "What about *this* one?" rather than "What about *his* one?"

19. singular / plural

The incorrect word here is "its". This word is used with a singular subject (just one person or one thing) to tell us that someone or something belongs to *it*. For example, "The cat finished its dinner" (the "dinner" belongs to "The cat"). However, because the subject of the sentence is "dresses" (plural) the possessive word needs to reflect this, so we would use "their" instead of "its". It should read: "Since the dresses are meant to be classic and elegant, *their* designers have spent …" If the writer had written: "Since the dress …" (singular) we would then need to talk about "its designers …", using singular possessive determiner "its": "Since the dress is meant to be classic and elegant, *its* designers have spent ..."

20. articles

The article "the" is not really necessary in the second sentence. Mr. Newell could have said: "... from September 20th ..." or "... from the 20th September ...", but not "... from the September 20th ..."

21. apostrophes

There should be an apostrophe after "12 months" because "half price line rental" belongs to, or is related to, "12 months". This sentence literally means: "12 months *of* half price line rental". If the offer was less generous and only gave 1 month of half price line rental, you would be able to see the need for an apostrophe more clearly: "1 month's half price line rental". It wouldn't look right if we put "1 months half price line rental" because "months" (a plural form) cannot follow "1" (a singular form).

22. spelling

The mistake in this example is in the third sentence. We can talk about an "inability" to do something, but the word "inable" doesn't exist. The correct word in this sentence is "unable". The sentence should read: "They seem *unable* to know when it's time to end a track".

23. spelling

This example was adapted from a quotation printed on the front cover of an autobiography by a famous public figure. The word "theif" should be spelled "thief".

24. apostrophes

The answer to this example is very similar to that of example no. 21. The meaning of the sentence is: "What would you say to 6 weeks *of* free DVD rental?" If we use "of" then we don't need an apostrophe. If we remove "of" to shorten the sentence (perhaps to make it flow better) then we need to add an apostrophe to show that the two phrases ("6 weeks" and "free DVD rental") are related to each other. We wouldn't write: "1 weeks free DVD rental". It would look wrong, and we would know to add an apostrophe between "week" and "s". But when it is more than one week (plural "weeks") it is less clear what to do – whether to add an apostrophe or not – and so some of us simply leave it out. This is a very common mistake which can be seen on posters or leaflets in virtually any mobile phone shop, or car dealership in the country; indeed anywhere where you can get: "12 months interest free credit" or "2 years servicing free of charge". Both of these sentences need an apostrophe (after "months" and "years"). If you can put the word "of" after the number of weeks, months or years, then you need to use an apostrophe. For example: "12 months *of* interest free credit" can be shortened to: "12 months' interest free credit". The apostrophe comes after the "s" in these examples because there is more than one month and year. We couldn't write "12 month's …" because the word month must have an "s" to make it plural, because there is more than one month.

25. punctuation

In this example there is a comma missing from after "games" in the last line. If you want to make a list of items, you need to use a comma to separate each one. The last line should read: "... you'll have easy access to all your music, games, films and photos – instantly!" This makes the sentence easier to read, because all the items in the list are now neatly prevented from running into each other by the commas. Apart from the last two items in the list, which are separated by "and". Some people would put a comma before "and" as well, but this isn't necessary. A good list needs a comma after each item, apart from the second to last item, which is followed by "and", then the final item. Like this:

"My favourite sports are: football, rugby, sailing and wrestling."

26. singular / plural

The mistake comes in the second paragraph, where the word "critic" should be the plural "critics". If we wanted to write "music critic" – singular – we would have to use an article to show that we meant just one, i.e. "a music critic". It's unlikely that a short entertainment news item like this would refer to just one music critic; rather the article wants to get across the feeling that a consensus has been reached about Mr Williams's illustrious career in music by a whole gaggle of music critics.

27. spelling

A misspelled logo, similar to the one in this example, could be seen for several hours in the top right-hand corner of the screen during programmes broadcast by a well-known music channel. That is, until someone at the channel spotted the mistake – or perhaps a viewer called in and told them about it – and the misspelled word "Carribean" was replaced with the correctly spelled: "Caribbean".

28. doesn't make sense

The first sentence of this article simply doesn't make sense. Perhaps a sub-editor working on this top-ranking news website had hastily edited the article and put it back online with a few vital phrases missing – without checking it properly. Perhaps the intention of the author for the first sentence was something like this (although other answers would fit as well): "Historian Daniel Parkinson has *described his decision to take* fifteen years to write a new book about the Battle of Trafalgar as simply being one of artistic integrity". This fits because there is now an object to the sentence – "his decision" – which relates to "one" later on in the sentence. Using "one" is a shorter way to write, because there is no need to repeat the abstract noun "decision". We wouldn't write: "Historian Daniel Parkinson has described his decision to take fifteen years to write a new book about the Battle of Trafalgar as simply being *a decision* of artistic integrity". We know that the author is talking about the "decision" when they write "one". But in the original example there isn't a noun (any *thing*) earlier on in the sentence for the "one" to relate to.

29. apostrophes

In this example, there should be an apostrophe after "women" to indicate possession, because the "clothes sale" belongs to, or is related to the "women". The sentence should read: "WOMEN'S CLOTHES SALE". "Women" is a plural word, meaning more than one woman, so we can assume that the sale features clothes that are suitable for more than one woman. The word "women" is already plural (despite not having an "s" at the end), so there is no such word as "womens". "Womens" is not plural of the word "woman". It is a made up word. It is clear that the author meant "womens" as "women" plus possessive apostrophe "s". They just forgot to use the apostrophe.

30. punctuation

As well as helping us to separate items in a list, the comma is used to separate clauses in sentences. This is so that the sentences are easier to read and the author's intended meaning is clearer. In general, punctuation helps us to organise our words and make what we want to express easier to understand. The mistake in this example comes in the last sentence. The words "it seemed" are a separate clause within this sentence, and as such should be separated from the rest of the sentence by two commas. The author has added one comma, but forgot to add the second, after "seemed". The sentence should read: "Sydney, it seemed, was a city of striking contrasts". Here is a similar use of commas to separate clauses within a sentence: "The bus, which was late, came bouncing down the road at breakneck speed". The clause "which was late" gives us useful information about the context of the arrival of the bus. We need to separate this clause from the rest of the sentence to make it easier to read – the action becomes clearer. If we didn't use commas at all it would read like this: "The bus which was late came bouncing down the road at breakneck speed", which isn't very clear, and is certainly harder to read.

31. punctuation

This example shows a style error: a use of punctuation which is unnecessary, or doesn't look very nice and which doesn't add anything to the information that the author is trying to put across, namely the four exclamation marks after "Sunday 16th April". It isn't necessary to put even one exclamation mark after this date, but clearly the author wanted to draw our attention to the date, and felt that four exclamation marks was the best way to achieve this. The result, though, looks silly because three of the exclamation marks are redundant. Only teenage girls writing top secret diaries should be allowed to sprinkle punctuation marks around so freely. Not adults who are writing for adult readers, and certainly not authors of cathedral newsletters!!!! See, it does look a bit silly and breathless, doesn't it? Of course, this is not a mistake; it's rather a style error, and these are sometimes in the eye of the beholder. For example, some readers may feel strangely exhilarated by seeing such a liberal and uncensored use of the exclamation mark. Similar style errors include: "Excessive use of the exclamation mark and question mark together!???!!??!!" to indicate disbelief, and: "Using 'smileys' after everything you write ;o))" These things are fine when writing for family or friends, when writing informal emails and text messages or even just for your own pleasure, but they start to look patronising and out of place when they appear in something that has been written for a wider audience; particularly an adult audience.

32. articles

The mistake in this example comes in the second sentence, where the wrong article is used before "idea". Because this word starts with a vowel sound, the indefinite article should be "an" rather than "a". The sentence should read: "Tonight, a student from Wales has *an* idea for …"

33. singular /plural

The word "What's …" is a short form (or contraction) of the verb "to be". The full form is "What is …" "Is" is a singular form of this verb ("he is, she is, it is"), while "are" is a plural form ("we are", "they are"). For this reason, you can't follow "What's …" with a plural noun such as "chances". It is necessary to change the verb to the plural form "What're …" (which is a contraction of "What are …") so that the corrected sentence reads: "What*'re* the chances of a manned mission to Mars?"

34. spelling

There is a spelling mistake on the fourth line of this example. The word "closedown" should read "close down". "To close down" is a verb form (a phrasal verb, which means a verb ("close") with a preposition ("down") working together as one verb or one action). The sentence is describing the action that the store will take (i.e. it will close down). The author has incorrectly used "closedown", which is a noun that describes the process of closing down. For example, this would be fine: "There will be a closedown in our store at 6 pm". There is a clue that "closedown" is a noun here because it requires an article. "Close down", on the other hand, is correct for our example because it's a verb and fits together with "will" to complete the future tense verb form, which begins with the subject: "Our existing store …", continues with the verb phrase: "… will close down …" and ends with an adverbial clause (showing the time): "… at 6.00pm on Saturday 17th June".

35. apostrophes

This is a straightforward case of a missing apostrophe. The "Life" belongs to the "Child" – the two words are related – so there must be a possessive apostrophe "s" after "Child". We know that the plural form of the noun "Child" would be "Children", which tells us there is no such word as "Childs" – it isn't in the dictionary; it isn't the plural of "Child". The sentence should read: "Improve a Child's Life".

36. doesn't make sense

On the face of things, this table of British Prime Ministers looks totally bona fide and makes for fascinating reading. However, if you study the dates closely you will find that one of these illustrious political leaders is out of synch with his cohorts. The dates don't match up. According to these dates George Grenville was Prime Minister before the Earl of Bute, but the dates are round the wrong way, because the Earl was actually Prime Minister between 1762-63, while Grenville (whose nickname in Parliament was "Gentle Shepherd", incidentally) was Prime Minister between 1763-65. It always pays to double-check all the data before you publish complicated tables of factual information.

37. punctuation

Here's an example where the author has tried to use an apostrophe correctly, but instead ended up using a single speech mark incorrectly. "Baby of the Year '05" should read: "Baby of the Year '05". In the example the author has put a single speech mark before "05" when they clearly meant to use an apostrophe. The difference is that the tail of the apostrophe points the opposite way to the tail of the single speech mark. Some word-processing programs help to make this a common error because when you type apostrophe followed by "05" you will normally get: '05. This is because the program assumes that you are writing something enclosed in single speech marks and automatically provides you with the first part of the single speech marks – which is not the apostrophe that you wanted. Sometimes it is necessary to show the word-processing program who's boss!

38. apostrophes

This special promotion for students, sponsored by a major UK bank, has been running for years and is promoted by hundreds of thousands of glossy leaflets and posters – all of them missing an apostrophe after "person". It's enough to make a "person" really frustrated! The correct phrase should be: "a free 4-year Young Person*'s* Travel Card". We know this because the "Travel Card" belongs to the "Young Person" – or at least it will if they apply for this special offer. In this example, "Person" is a singular noun. Nobody uses the word "persons" to describe more than one person (plural); we would say "people" instead. If the author of this promotion wanted to use the plural word "people", they would still have to employ the services of an apostrophe – "Young People*'s* Travel Card" – because the "Travel Card" still belongs to the "Young People". It's not good enough to go on printing "Young Persons Travel Card" on hundreds of thousands of leaflets and posters year after year and just hope for the best that no one will spot this easily-corrected mistake.

39. spelling

In this example the mistake comes in the last line, where "every day" should be "everyday". The difference is important: "every day" is an adverbial describing a period of time when something happens. For example, "I go for a walk *every day*". On the other hand, "everyday" is an adjective which is used before a noun to describe something that is ordinary or run-of-the-mill or normal, for example: "Shop at Debbie's – for *everyday* value and service". The sentence should read: "… be able to participate with confidence in all sorts of everyday situations".

40. doesn't make sense

There is a short word missing from the second sentence; before "make" it is necessary to add the word "to". We always talk about having the chance *to* … something. For example, "The chance to make … / to go … / to do … / to own …, and so on. The sentence should read: "Children will have the chance to make their own models …"

41. spelling

There is a spelling mistake in paragraph 4. – "we'll *Isend* you more!" should read "we'll *send* you more!" Clearly this is a typing or editing error rather than a straightforward misspelling. Perhaps the extra "I" had belonged to the previous word – "we'll" – in an earlier draft of the text. This mistake should have been picked up when the leaflet was proof-read, but wasn't, and as a consequence appeared on hundreds of thousands of leaflets which were distributed inside a variety of top-selling glossy magazines.

42. apostrophes

There shouldn't be an apostrophe in the word "one's" because this word is the plural form of "one". It doesn't have a possessive relationship with the word that follows and it isn't part of a verb form (verb "to be" – "one is …"). In this sentence "ones" refers to the word "pictures" from the previous sentence and is in the plural form because "pictures" is plural – more than one picture. We can talk about choosing "the one you want" – which indicates one thing (singular) or "the ones you want", depending on whether what you are talking about (in this case "your pictures") is singular or plural. The sentence should read: "… review your pictures on screen and choose the ones you want".

43. punctuation

The problem with punctuation in this example comes in the title: "What the Heritage Committee is doing about it?" If you take away the question mark at the end, this sentence is fine. After reading this title you would expect to be able to read all about what the heritage committee is doing about "it" – whatever "it" is. But if the author intended to ask a question, this sentence is incorrect because it doesn't use a question form. To make a question form you would need to invert the verb ("to be"), which means putting it before the subject of the sentence ("the Heritage Committee") rather than after. So the title could read either: "What the Heritage Committee is doing about it" (*without* the question mark) or "What *is* the Heritage Committee doing about it?" (*with* the question mark) – depending on what the author wanted to write in the article that follows.

44. spelling

The spelling mistake in this example comes in the first sentence. "… a much high quality selection of games …" should read: "… a much *higher* quality selection of games …" The reason for this is that we can't use a simple adjective like "high" with "much". We need to use the comparative form of the adjective – "higher" – because the sentence is making a comparison. It's comparing the number of games and movies available now with the many more titles that will be available by Christmas. We could see the full comparative sentence if the author had completed the comparison by using: "than they have now" at the end of the sentence. For example: "By Christmas, owners of the new Channel Hoppa console will have a much higher quality selection of games and movies from which to choose *than they have now*". However, this is excessively wordy and the meaning of the sentence is clear without using "than..."

45. apostrophes

There is an apostrophe missing from the end of "minutes" in the last line of this example. If the author had written "50 minutes away" an apostrophe after "minutes" wouldn't be necessary because "50 minutes" is a straightforward adverbial phrase, describing the distance between two places by reference to a period of time. Because the author puts in a noun – "drive" – after the adverbial phrase ("50 minutes") they create a possessive relationship between the "50 minutes" and the "drive". The meaning becomes: "50 minutes of driving …" We can test out the need for an apostrophe here by looking at what would happen if the minutes were reduced to just one minute: "1 minute's drive". We still need an apostrophe; we couldn't write "1 minutes drive" because since "1" is singular it cannot be followed by the plural noun form "minutes". The author could have used the more straightforward phrase: "a 50 minute drive away from …" but "50 minutes' drive away" must include an apostrophe after "minutes" (the plural form, because there are fifty of them) to be grammatically correct.

46. spelling

This spelling mistake, spotted on a leaflet at a large country hotel, was probably a typing mistake which wasn't corrected when the leaflet was proofread – if it was proofread at all. When spelling the time we wouldn't write "1 O'clock" with a capital "O", but rather with all lower case letters, like this: "1 o'clock". This mistake may have been caused by an over-eager word-processing program, which automatically altered the "o" in "o'clock" – perhaps it thought it was starting a new sentence. New sentences always start with a capital letter. It shows the value of sitting down with whatever you have just typed and printed off the computer and spending a few minutes reading it through slowly, looking for straightforward mistakes like this one. Those extra few minutes spent proof-reading – and then perhaps editing and reprinting your work – will really pay dividends, because the image that your work projects afterwards will be far more professional.

47. punctuation

The punctuation mistake in this example can be found in the last sentence, where there is a single space missing between the words "Mr" and "&". It should read: "… Margaret Smeghurst handed over first prize of a bottle of bubbly to *Mr & Mrs* Halliwell …" It is important to remember to put a single space between each word in a sentence. In this example, "&" should be treated as a separate word ("and"), even though it represents "and" as a symbol.

48. spelling

The misspelled word in this example is "programme". In the UK we use the word "programme" as a noun (a thing) to talk primarily about something on television or radio, e.g. "a television programme". The author of this advert tries to use the common noun "programme" as a verb, when the verb form should be spelled with the American English spelling: "program". In American English the noun form ("TV program") and verb form ("to program your VCR") are spelled the same, while in British English there is still this distinction, perhaps because the verb "to program" is still relatively new to us. The sentence should read: "*Program* your 10 favourite tracks". It is worth noting that in British English we do use "program" as a common noun when talking about computer software, e.g. "a new computer program for word-processing".

49. apostrophes

The problem with apostrophes comes in the third sentence, which should read: "The students' union has *its* own facilities on both campuses …" We use the word "its" because "its" is a possessive form which describes the relationship between "The students' union" and "facilities on both campuses". The facilities belong to the students' union. The word "it's" is completely different. It is a verb form, which can indicate not one but two verbs – either verb "to be", as in "it is", or verb "to have", as in "it has". "Its" is a possessive adjective, like "my", "your", "his", "her", "our" and "their", which relates to the pronoun "it", meaning a thing, an object or a place. In fact, anything which doesn't have a gender (male or female). "The students' union" is a place, an inanimate object which doesn't have a gender, so the right possessive form to use is "its".

50. punctuation

The punctuation mistake comes in the second to last sentence, which starts "Above all …" The problem is with the comma, which has been put in the wrong place. It should be used to separate the two clauses: "Above all …" and the rest of the sentence, so that the sentence should read: "Above all, this means that many teachers have had to …" Commas are helpful in sentences because they separate clauses, making what is written easier to read. Imagine a comma as half a pause and a full stop as a full pause. Now read this sentence aloud, leaving half a pause where the comma is: "Above all this, means that many teachers have had to go "back to school" themselves…" It doesn't sound right, does it? Now read it aloud again, with the comma after "Above all" instead of "this". It should sound much better this time.

51. singular / plural

The problem here is the phrase: "there are a staggering amount of things to see …" Although the author is talking about many *things*, the noun phrase ("staggering amount of things") starts with a singular article – "a". This is because the word "amount", which is the main noun here, is in singular form. It is "amount" rather than the plural "amounts". As a consequence, "there are …", which uses a plural verb ("are" – from verb "to be") must be changed to "there is …", using the singular verb "is". The phrase should read: "there *is* a staggering amount of things to see …"

52. apostrophes

According to this advertisement there is going to be just one child with really active fingers this Christmas! The advert begins: "Get the *kid's* little fingers active this Christmas …", using "kid" (which is singular) then the possessive apostrophe "s". The author implores us to get *one* kid's little fingers active, rather than *many* kids' little fingers. It's hard to believe that this is what they meant because it stands to reason that they would want to sell more than one funky farm activity set. If we change the noun "kid" to "kids" (plural form) and put the apostrophe after the plural form the sentence would be correct, and would read: "Get the *kids'* little fingers active this Christmas …" With plural nouns like this it isn't necessary to use an "s" after the possessive apostrophe. Look at this example: "The car's wheels". If we changed the singular noun "car" to the plural "cars", we wouldn't need to write: "The cars's wheels" – simply "The cars' wheels" is enough.

53. spelling

The spelling mistake in this example comes near the end, in the sentence that begins: "I got the feeling that …" The phrase "Lloyd and is trademark slapstick routines" should read "Lloyd and *his* trademark slapstick routines". The word "is" is a verb (from verb "to be") and is incorrect in this sentence because the possessive adjective "his" is required, to indicate the fact that the "trademark slapstick routines" belong to "Lloyd".

54. spelling

In this example the word "beleive" should be spelled "believe". I couldn't "believe" it myself when I saw that this cartoon had been published in a national newspaper and no one had spotted this mistake prior to publication. Or perhaps they had noticed it but deemed it unimportant and not worth correcting. We will never know.

55. articles

On the third line down it is necessary to change the article "A" to "An", because the word that follows ("Easter") begins with a vowel sound rather than a consonant sound. The sentence should read: "An Easter Message".

56. apostrophes

This example is adapted from a large, colour advertisement which was printed in several different national newspapers for several weeks. Clearly no one involved with the advert minded that it used an incorrect punctuation mark before the word "Ello". The word "Ello" was printed in very large type, in italics, which amplified the mistake by making it more noticeable. This word needs an apostrophe before it to indicate that it has been shortened – from the full greeting *Hello* to the more informal, or colloquial *'Ello*. The author of this ad has used a single speech mark: ' (which has a tail that points to the right), instead of an apostrophe: ' (which has a tail that points to the left). The sentence should read: *'Ello Jeff*, rather than *'Ello Jeff*. This mistake is similar to the one in example number 37 in that it was probably caused by a word-processing package working away on auto-pilot and not understanding that the author wanted to put an apostrophe before "Ello", rather than a single speech mark. Alternatively, perhaps the well-paid advertising executives working away busily on this campaign don't know the difference between a single speech mark and an apostrophe. Or maybe they just wanted the company they were representing to look really unprofessional. We may never know!

57. spelling

The spelling mistake in this example can be found on the last line: "managment" should be spelled "management". Since any spellchecker would have highlighted this error, it's hard to understand how it slipped through the net and ended up published in the final version of the advertisement.

58. apostrophes

In this example there is an apostrophe missing after "someone". The sentence should read: "Drink someone*'s* milkshake". The "milkshake" belongs to "someone" – it is "someone's". There is a possessive relationship between "milkshake" and "someone" which it is necessary to show by using the possessive apostrophe "s" after the person to whom it belongs – in this case, that person is "someone".

59. doesn't make sense

There is a stray "everyone" in the third sentence of this piece of text. The third sentence should begin: "Everyone at People Power plays an enormously important role in helping ordinary people …" This mistake may have been made when the author was editing the piece, although if they had spent just a few minutes checking their work carefully after creating it, rather than hastily publishing it, they would probably have spotted the unnecessary word. This newsletter would have been distributed to many different offices of the same national training company. Potentially several thousand employees would have received a copy. Whether they read it or not is another matter, but wouldn't it have been better to spend those extra few minutes checking for that stray "everyone"? We all make mistakes when producing written work. We make some because we are not sure how to use certain punctuation marks and others because we are unclear about a particular grammar rule. But we can all eliminate the majority of our mistakes – the "little mistakes", like the one in this example – if we spend time learning about the kind of mistakes that we make and take just ten minutes to check what we've written – to proof-read our work – before we publish it and make it accessible for a wider audience.

60. spelling

The spelling mistake in this example comes in the last sentence, where the word "past" should be spelled "passed". The words "past" and "passed" are homophones, which means that they sound the same but have different spellings and different meanings. "Past" can be used as an adjective, adverb, preposition or noun; for example, "the past" (i.e. yesterday, last week, etc.) is a noun (a thing). "Passed" should be used here as a past participle verb – it belongs to the present perfect verb phrase "Sales have passed …" The sentence should read: "Sales of his latest release, Never Be Lonely (When You've Got A Friend), have now *passed* the 2 million mark in the UK alone."

A-Z of English Grammar Words

Adjectives are describing words. We use them to describe nouns (things). For example: *the **tall** building / an **interesting** novel / a **short** conversation / a **new** year, etc.*

An **Adverbial Clause** is part of a sentence which tells us how or when something happened. For example, "I woke up **at seven o'clock**".

Adverbs describe the verb in a sentence – the action, how something is being done. For example, "Maria spoke **loudly**". In this sentence, "spoke" is the verb/action and "loudly" describes how the verb/action was done.

The English **alphabet** has 26 letters. There are 5 vowels – **a**, **e**, **i**, **o** and **u**. The remaining 21 letters are called consonants – **b**, **c**, **d**, **f**, **g**, **h**, **j**, **k**, **l**, **m**, **n**, **p**, **q**, **r**, **s**, **t**, **v**, **w**, **x**, **y** and **z**.

There are three **articles** in the English language: "a" and "an" (indefinite articles) and "the" (definite article). We normally use an article before a common noun (an everyday object or thing). We use "a" and "an" when the noun is non-specific – e.g. "A school in Cambridge" – and we use "the" if we are talking about a particular thing, something that we are already aware we're talking about – e.g. "*The* school in Cambridge". We use "an" before words that start with a *vowel sound* and "a" before words that start with a *consonant sound*.

We use **clauses** to make sentences. There may be several clauses in one sentence. For example:

"The weather was nice, so we went for a picnic."

In this sentence there are two clauses: the *main clause* ("The weather was nice") and a *subordinate clause* ("so we went for a picnic"). The clauses are separated by a comma. A subordinate clause gives extra information about the main clause. A subordinate clause can't be a separate sentence on its own, while a main clause can. A subordinate clause needs a main clause for it to make sense.

Conjunctions are words that link together clauses and phrases in a sentence. Words like: "and", "because", "but", "or", and "so". For example: "I didn't enjoy watching all the rubbish on television, **so** I gave away my set to a local school **and** cancelled my TV licence".

Consonants are the 21 letters of the alphabet which are not vowels, namely: **b**, **c**, **d**, **f**, **g**, **h**, **j**, **k**, **l**, **m**, **n**, **p**, **q**, **r**, **s**, **t**, **v**, **w**, **x**, **y**, and **z**.

A **consonant sound** is the sound made by a word which begins with a consonant, for example: "**c**at", "**d**og", and "**m**ouse". This includes the "yuh" sound at the beginning of some words which start with the vowel "u", like "university", "union", "uniform" and "unicycle". This is why we say, "*a* university" and "*a* union" rather than "*an* university" and "*an* union". Although these words begin with a vowel, they don't begin with a vowel *sound*, so we have to use article "a" rather than "an".

A **contraction** is the short form (or *contracted form*) of a verb. For example: "I'll" is a contraction of "I will", "She'd" is a contraction of "She had" and "Jeff's" is a contraction of either "Jeff is" or "Jeff has".

A **determiner** is a word that goes before a noun to give further information about that noun. For example, in the phrase "some eggs", "some" is a determiner which matches the plural noun "eggs". We know from the plural determiner "some" and the plural "s" at the end of "egg" that there is more than one "egg". Other common determiners include: articles ("**the** egg", "**an** egg"), possessive determiners ("**my** egg", "**her** egg"), question words ("**which** eggs?", "**whose** eggs?") and quantity words ("**many** eggs", "**more** eggs").

An **infinitive verb** is the basic form of a verb. For example, "To go" is an infinitive verb, while "I go" (present simple tense), "I went" (past simple tense) and "I was going" (past continuous tense) are all ways of using the same basic form of the verb to show action happening at different times or in different tenses.

Inversion – which literally means reversal – is the word we use in English grammar to describe what happens to the word order of a sentence if we change it from a statement to a question. For example, this sentence is a statement: "Melinda is a qualified pilot". To make this statement into a question we need to swap around the verb ("is") and subject ("Melinda"), like this: "Is Melinda a qualified pilot?" We must also change the full stop of the statement into a question mark. It is helpful to remember inversion when writing statements and question forms. "He has ..." is inverted to become "Has he ...?" (question form), "You could..." is inverted to become "Could you ...?" (question form) and "They didn't ..." is inverted to become "Didn't they ...?" (question form), and so on.

its and it's are often confused, perhaps because they sound the same. However, they have completely different meanings and functions within a sentence. "Its" is the possessive adjective which indicates that something belongs to "it", for example: "The dog finished **its** dinner and went outside". "It's" is a contracted form of either verb to be ("it is") or verb to have ("it has"). For example: "**It's** a nice day, isn't it?" ("*It is* a nice day, isn't it?") or "**It's** been a nice day, hasn't it?" ("*It has* been a nice day, hasn't it?").

A **letter** is one part of a word. There are 26 letters in the English alphabet, ranging from "a" to "z". We normally need to use more than one letter to make a word, although the letter "I" on its own is a word ("**I** like you") and so is the letter "a" ("I like you **a** lot").

We use the term **lower case** to describe small letters. There are two *cases* in the English alphabet: *lower case* (small letters) and *upper case* (capital letters or big letters). We normally start a sentence with a capital letter, but then continue using only small letters, apart from for abbreviations (e.g. "ITV") and for words which always start with a capital letter, like names of people, places and companies. These words are called *proper nouns*.

Nouns are things. There are lots of different kinds of nouns:

Common nouns are everyday things which we can see and touch (like "table", "chair", "coat" and "swimming pool").

Proper nouns are words which always start with a capital letter, like the names of people, places, companies, days and months (for example: "Eric Morrison", "Birmingham", "The Forth Bridge", "The Royal Shakespeare Company", "Monday" and "February").

Abstract nouns are things that we can't see or touch but are there all the same. They describe things like feelings ("happiness" and "love"), qualities ("loyalty" and "weakness") or concepts ("democracy" and "peace").

Countable nouns (also known as "count nouns") are things which have plural forms – i.e. they can be counted using numbers. For example: "one bag, two bags", or "one mobile phone, two mobile phones".

Uncountable nouns (also known as "noncount nouns") are things which are not separate items and cannot be counted. We don't know how many of them there are. For example: "bread", "A slice of bread" or "Some bread" not "a bread" or "two breads".

A **paragraph** is a chunk of text which is made up of several different sentences. If you are reading a novel there could be three paragraphs on one page with about four or five different sentences in each paragraph.

Phrases are parts of a sentence and are used to make clauses. They are made up of one or more words and there are different types, for example:

noun phrases – e.g. "fish and chips"

verb phrases – e.g. " eats", "is eating", "has eaten", "has been eating"

prepositional phrases – e.g. "in the kitchen"

We use the **plural form** of a noun when there is more than one of it. For example, if there is more than one "table" we use the plural form, which is "tables". We can make the *regular plural* form of most nouns by adding "s" to the end of the word (e.g. one "bed" becomes two "beds", and one "pen" becomes two "pens"). Some nouns have an *irregular plural* form, so we have to add different endings, like "es" (e.g. one "box" becomes two "boxes" and one "church" becomes two "churches"). For nouns that end in "y" we usually replace the "y" with "ies" (e.g. one "party" becomes two "parties" and one "strawberry" becomes two "strawberries"). There are a few other irregular plural endings, e.g. nouns ending in "f" have the plural ending "ves" ("loaf" becomes "loaves"), and there are some nouns that have their own unique plural form, e.g. one "child" becomes two "children" and one "mouse" becomes two "mice".

We use **possessive apostrophe "s"** after a name and before a noun (a thing) to show that this thing belongs to the name. For example: "Julie**'s** schoolbook" (the "schoolbook belongs to "Julie") and "Scunthorpe United**'s** loyal supporters" (the "loyal supporters" belong to "Scunthorpe United").

A **preposition** is a word that describes where something is. For example, "**in** the kitchen", "**under** the stairs", "**on** the table" and "**opposite** the bank".

Personal subject pronouns

Personal subject pronouns are words which go before a verb to replace nouns (the name of somebody or something). For example, instead of saying "Robbie said ..." you could use the personal subject pronoun "he" to make: "He said ...", or instead of saying "The university library was closed" you could use the personal subject pronoun "it" to make: "It was closed". We use these words in place of nouns when it is clear what or who you are talking about. The personal subject pronouns in English are: **I**, **you**, **he**, **she**, **it**, **we**, and **they**.

Possessive determiners

Possessive determiners – **my**, **your**, **his**, **her**, **its**, **our** and **their** – are words that give us information about who owns what, for example: "This is **my** banana and that's your **coconut**".

We use the different symbols called **punctuation marks** to make our writing easier to read. For example, without punctuation marks we wouldn't know where one sentence finished and another began. Some of the most commonly used punctuation marks are:

. *full stop*. We put a full stop at the end of each sentence, unless it is a question or needs an exclamation mark (e.g. "My uncle lives in Newfoundland**.**"). It is also used with abbreviations (e.g. "**e.g.**").

, *comma*. We use commas to separate clauses in a sentence (e.g. "I might catch the ten o'clock train**,** if I hurry up", and to separate words in a list (e.g. "I would like a bag of crisps**,** two tubs of ice-cream, a can of fizzy orange and a large box of popcorn, please.").

' *apostrophe*. We use an apostrophe before an "s" to show that something belongs to someone or something else (e.g. "Letitia**'s** stapler") or to show that part of a word is missing, e.g. with contracted verb forms, like "It**'s** raining" (the apostrophe replaces the "i" of "is raining") and "Paul**'s** gone home early" (the apostrophe replaces the "ha" of "has gone").

? *question mark*. A question mark is used at the end of a question, instead of a full stop (e.g. "What time does the film start**?**").

! *exclamation mark*. We put the exclamation mark at the end of a sentence which has a stronger emphasis than other sentences. It may be that the sentence is amusing (e.g. "My dog has no nose. How does he smell? Terrible!") or insulting (e.g. "I'm sorry but your dog really *does* stink!") or any sentence that conveys a strong emotion (e.g. "Oh no! Someone's stolen my MP3 player!").

" " *speech marks*. Speech marks go around part of a text which is spoken by someone. This is to make it stand out from the rest of the text. E.g.

The mechanic had a good look inside the bonnet and said, "There's no hope, I'm afraid. You don't need a mechanic, you need a miracle worker!" I tried to hide my disappointment. "OK", I replied.

; *semi-colon*. A semi-colon is a short pause in a sentence. It is not as long a pause as a full stop, but it's longer than a comma. For example, if you read the following piece of text out loud, you could count two beats for a full stop, one beat for a semi-colon and half a beat for a comma: "The boys started running, but they were soon out of breath; it wasn't long before the gang caught up with them".

: *colon*. A colon is similar to a semi-colon in that it helps to divide a sentence and provides a longer pause than a comma, but about half the pause of a full stop. It is used differently because it shows that the clause which comes after it follows on from the clause before it. For example, in the sentence: "The children opened their present: they couldn't believe what they found!" the idea in the second clause ("they couldn't believe ...") follows on from the action in the first clause ("The children opened their present ..."). Using a colon is like saying, "There's more to come in the next part of the sentence". It provides a short pause in a sentence and points the way to a continuing thought or action.

( ) *brackets*. We can use brackets to slip extra information into a sentence, without disturbing the flow of the sentence too much. For example: "It had been John's idea to invite Becky (who was secretly in love with him) to Heather's birthday party". Brackets are known as *parentheses* in American English.

- *hyphen*. We use a hyphen to join together two related words (for example: "post-Impressionism" and "south-west") and to write numbers as words (for example "35" becomes "thirty-five"). It is also used at the end of a line to show that a word continues on the next line, e.g. "fre-quently", and to indicate distances between times ("1914-1918") and places ("London-Brighton").

— *dash*. A dash is longer than a hyphen and has a different job. We use it to separate a particular clause from the rest of a sentence, for example: "We had been to Frankfurt four times – five if you count changing flights once on the way to Sydney – but had never spent New Year's Eve there". It is also used to indicate a pause or a change in the sentence's train of thought, for example: "Roger took off his socks thoughtfully – it had been an extremely trying day".

/   forward slash. We use the forward slash when writing the address of a page on the internet, for example: "https://purlandtraining.com/"

A **question form** is used to make a sentence that asks a question, for example: "What time is it?" These sentences end with a question mark instead of a full stop. Question forms often begin with "wh-" question words, like "**who**", "**what**", "**where**", "**when**", "**why**", "**which**" and "**how**". "How" can be considered an honorary "wh-" question word because it contains both the letters "w" and "h"!

A **sentence** is a self-contained group of words which begins with a capital letter ("A", "B", "C", etc.) and ends with a full stop ("."), question mark ("?") or exclamation mark ("!"). For example:

Derby County's astonishing unbeaten run at home continued unabated.

We use the **singular form** of a noun when there is just one of it. For example, one "table" ("tables" would be the regular plural form) and one "tooth" ("teeth" is the irregular plural form).

Subject-Verb-Object is the phrase used to describe a common sentence structure in English. In the sentence: "The children are eating ice-creams", "The children" is the subject, "are eating" is the verb form (the action – what the subject is doing) and "ice-creams" is the object (the thing that is having the action done to it).

We use the term **upper case** to describe capital letters (or *big letters*). We normally start a sentence with a capital letter, but then use small letters for the rest of the words, apart from abbreviations and words which always start with a capital letter, like names of people, places and companies.

Verbs are action words, or *doing words*. They tell us what somebody or something is doing in a sentence. For example, in the sentence "John washed his car", "washed" is the verb, or action, John is the person doing the action (the *subject*), and "his car" is the thing that is having the action done to it (the *object*). Verbs can be regular and irregular. Most verbs are *regular*, which means that they all follow the same rules, for example when forming the past tense all regular verbs end with "ed" ("walk" becomes "walked" and "play" becomes "played", and so on). However, some very common verbs are *irregular*, which means they don't follow the same rules as regular verbs and you just have to learn their forms separately. Common irregular verbs are: "to be", "to do", "to have" and "to go". These four verbs are also the most common auxiliary verbs. Auxiliary verbs are helping verbs: they help a main verb to form a verb phrase. In this sentence: "Ricky and Jessica are teaching their daughter to swim", "are" is an auxiliary verb (from verb "to be") which helps the main verb "teaching" (from verb "to teach").

There are several different **verb tenses** in the English language. It is worth being aware of (or, better still, *learning*) some common *verb tables* in each of the following tenses: **present simple**, **present continuous**, **present perfect**, **past simple**, **past continuous**, **past perfect** and **future forms** (e.g. "going to"). For example, let's look at the verb "to eat", which is an irregular verb:

(Note: these verb tables do not cover negative and question forms for each tense, which can also be studied, e.g. "I eat / I don't eat / Do I eat?" and so on.)

present simple tense verb table:

I eat, You eat, He eats, She eats, It eats, We eat, They eat

present continuous tense verb table (with verb "to be" in the present tense as an auxiliary verb):

I am eating, You are eating, He is eating, She is eating, It is eating, We are eating, They are eating

present perfect tense verb table (with verb "to have" in the present tense as an auxiliary verb):

I have eaten, You have eaten, He has eaten, She has eaten, It has eaten, We have eaten, They have eaten past simple tense verb table:

I ate, You ate, He ate, She ate, It ate, We ate, They ate

past continuous tense verb table (with verb "to be" in the past tense as an auxiliary verb):

I was eating, You were eating, He was eating, She was eating, It was eating, We were eating, They were eating

past perfect tense verb table (with verb "to have" in the past tense as an auxiliary verb):

I had eaten, You had eaten, He had eaten, She had eaten, It had eaten, We had eaten, They had eaten

future form with "going to" and verb "to be" in the present tense as an auxiliary verb:

I'm going to eat, You're going to eat, He's going to eat, She's going to eat, It's going to eat, We're going to eat, They're going to eat

future form with "will" in the present tense as an auxiliary verb:

I will eat, You will eat, He will eat, She will eat, It will eat, We will eat, They will eat

There are 5 **vowels** in the English alphabet: **a**, **e**, **i**, **o** and **u**. The other 21 letters of the alphabet are called *consonants*.

A **vowel sound** is the sound made by a word which begins with a vowel, for example: "**a**nimal", "**e**ducation", "**I**ndia", "**o**range" and "**u**mbrella".

A **word** is a part of a sentence made up of one or more letters. Words in a sentence are separated by a single space on either side. Several words with a capital letter at the beginning of the first one and a full stop after the last one together form a sentence.

CPSIA information can be obtained
at www.ICGtesting.com
Printed in the USA
LVHW062234210723
753033LV00008B/623